Character P...

selected by Brian Moses

Contents

Men and women

Creatures real and imagined

Children

LONGMAN

The old sea dog

I remember him as if it were yesterday, as he came plodding to the inn door, his sea-chest following behind him in a handbarrow; a tall, strong, heavy, nut-brown man; his tarry pigtail falling over the shoulders of his soiled blue coat; his hands ragged and scarred, with black, broken nails; and the sabre cut across one cheek, a dirty, livid white.

from *Treasure Island* by Robert Louis Stevenson

Delphine

Delphine had always been striking, but she grew into a sleek and strange beauty that was quite as arresting as Atalia's much vaunted glory, although her own made no songs as her sister's did. The dolphin's daughter often came down from her tower in the early mornings, before anyone was awake, and sat watching the dawn break over the wide sea. It was as though she was waiting for something; but whatever it was, it never came.

from *The Dolphin's Daughter*
by Alma Alexandra Hromić

Scrooge

Scrooge! a squeezing, wrenching, grasping, scraping, clutching, covetous old sinner! hard and sharp as flint, from which no steel had ever struck out generous fire; secret, and self-contained, and solitary as an oyster.

from *A Christmas Carol*
by Charles Dickens

Princess Savitri

Savitri was a beautiful
princess who lived in
India hundreds of
years ago. Her eyes
were like lotus flowers.
Her skin was the
colour of sunbeams.
Her hair was shining

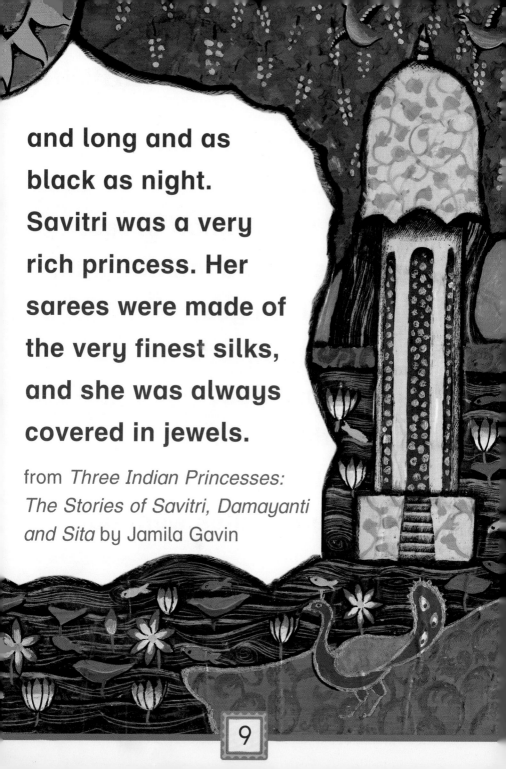

and long and as black as night. Savitri was a very rich princess. Her sarees were made of the very finest silks, and she was always covered in jewels.

from *Three Indian Princesses: The Stories of Savitri, Damayanti and Sita* by Jamila Gavin

The Pied Piper of Hamelin

His queer long coat from
   heel to head
Was half of yellow, half of red;
And he himself was tall and thin,
With sharp blue eyes,
   each like a pin,
And light loose hair,
   yet swarthy skin,
No tuft on cheek nor beard on chin,
But lips where smiles went out
   and in –
There was no guessing his kith
   and kin!

from *The Pied Piper of Hamelin* by Robert Browning

Miss Beckworth

She had grey hair and grey eyes and a grey and white blouse and a grey skirt and laced-up shoes, with a laced-up expression on her face to match. When she spoke her teeth were quite big and stuck out a bit, but I put all thoughts of Bugs Bunny imitations right out of my head.

There are some teachers – just a few – who have YOU'D BETTER NOT MESS WITH ME! tattooed right across their foreheads. She frowned at me with this incredibly fierce forehead and said, "Good morning. This isn't a very good start to the new school year."

from *The Lottie Project* by Jacqueline Wilson

My father

My father without the slightest
doubt, was the most marvellous
and exciting father any boy ever
had ... You might think, if you
didn't know him well, that he was a
stern and serious man. He wasn't.
He was actually a wildly funny
person. What made him appear so
serious was the fact that he never
smiled with his mouth. He did it all
with his eyes. He had brilliant blue
eyes and when he thought of
something funny, his eyes would

flash and if you looked carefully, you could actually see a tiny little golden spark dancing in the middle of each eye. But the mouth never moved.

from *Danny: The Champion of the World*
by Roald Dahl

The Queen of Narnia

... on a much higher seat in the middle of the sledge sat a very different person – a great lady, taller than any woman that Edmund had ever seen. She ... was covered in white fur up to her throat and held a long straight golden wand in her right hand and wore a golden crown on her head.

Her face was white – not merely pale, but white like snow or paper or icing-sugar, except for her very

red mouth. It was a beautiful face in other aspects, but proud and cold and stern.

from *The Lion, the Witch and the Wardrobe* by C. S. Lewis

17

The Birdman

He would be seen outside only
rarely in the daylight, perhaps
out in his rowing boat around the
island or sitting high on his cart;
and even in the hottest summers
he would always wear a black
cape over his shoulders and a
pointed black sou'wester on his
head. From a distance you could
hear him talking loudly to himself
in a strange, unearthly monotone.
Maybe it was not to himself that
he talked but to the kittiwake that

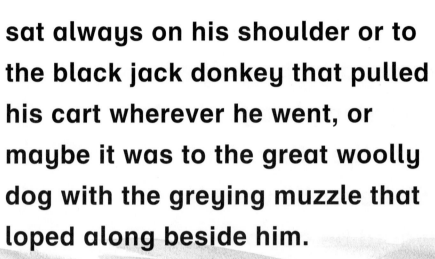

sat always on his shoulder or to the black jack donkey that pulled his cart wherever he went, or maybe it was to the great woolly dog with the greying muzzle that loped along beside him.

The Birdman went everywhere barefoot, even in winter, a stooped black figure that lurched as he walked, one step always shorter than the other. And wherever he went he would be surrounded by a flock of screaming seagulls that circled and floated about him, tirelessly vigilant, almost as if they were protecting him.

from *Why the Whales Came*
by Michael Morpurgo

The black fox

Her steps as she crossed the field were lighter and quicker than a cat's. As she came closer I could see that her black fur was tipped with white. It was as if it were midnight and the moon were shining on her fur, frosting it. The wind parted her fur as it changed directions. Suddenly she stopped. She was ten feet away now, and with the changing of the wind she got my scent. She looked right at me.

I did not move for a moment and neither did she. Her head was cocked to one side, her tail curled up, her front left foot raised. In all my life I never saw anything like that fox standing there with her pale green golden eyes on me and this great black fur being blown by the wind.

from *The Midnight Fox* by Betsy Byars

23

Yeti

He was gigantic and was covered in red hair from head to toe. Only the centre of his face was hairless. The skin was wrinkled and black. His nose was flat and turned up so that the nostrils were scarcely more than two holes in his face, and the chin receded almost formless into his neck.

His forehead was vast and prominent and overhung the face in a permanent frown. But under the thick red eyebrows the eyes that looked back down at me were searching and intelligent. They were wide with fear or anger – I could not tell which.

from *King of the Cloud Forests*
by Michael Morpurgo

A poisonous centipede

Belinda was ... a poisonous centipede. A very large one – a good eight inches long, or twenty centimetres, if you want to be metric about it. Just imagine, eight inches of shiny, black, swift-moving centipede – a twenty-centi-centipede! Her body was something like a caterpillar's in segments, but covered with hard, shiny, dark stuff – a sort of suit of armour, which is called a cuticle.

from *Harry the Poisonous Centipede*
by Lynne Reid Banks

The water horse

The first thing you noticed about it was its head, which was sticking out of the water on the end of quite a long neck. More than anything, it looked like a horse's head, with wide nostrils like a horse and even a suggestion of pricked ears. But its body was more like a turtle's. I don't mean it had a shell – it had a warty skin like a toad's, greeny-greyish in colour – but it had four flippers like a turtle has. And then it had a tail like a crocodile's. But just like you usually look at people's faces before you notice anything else about them, the thing that struck us was the look of its head. We didn't think about a crocodile or a toad or a turtle. We thought about a little horse.

from *The Water Horse* by Dick King-Smith

The Iron Man

Taller than a house, the Iron Man stood at the top of the cliff, on the very brink, in the darkness.

The wind sang through his iron fingers. His great iron head, shaped like a dustbin but as big as a bedroom, slowly turned to the right, slowly turned to the left. His iron ears turned, this way, that way. He was hearing the sea. His eyes, like headlamps, glowed white, then red, then infra-red, searching the sea.

from *The Iron Man* by Ted Hughes

Mishe-Nahma

There he lay in all his armour:
On each side a shield to guard him,
Plates of bone upon his forehead,
Down his sides and back
  and shoulders
Plates of bone with spines
  projecting!
Painted was he with his war-paints,
Stripes of yellow, red and azure,
Spots of brown and spots of sable;
And he lay there on the bottom,
Fanning with his fins of purple ...

from *The Song of Hiawatha*
by Henry Wadsworth Longfellow

Hobbits

They are (or were) a little people, about half our height, and smaller than the bearded Dwarves. Hobbits have no beards. There is little or no magic about them, except the ordinary everyday sort which helps them to disappear quietly and quickly when large stupid folk like you and me come blundering along, making a noise like elephants, which they can hear a mile off. They are inclined to be fat in the stomach; they dress in bright colours (chiefly green and yellow); wear no shoes, because their feet grow natural leathery soles and thick warm brown hair like the stuff on their heads (which is curly); have long clever brown fingers, good natured faces, and laugh deep fruity laughs (especially after dinner, which they have twice a day when they can get it).

from *The Hobbit* by J. R. Tolkien

Robin

Robin was not anything much, except four years old, and he looked a lot younger; probably because nothing ever happened to him ... He wore balaclava helmets and bobble hats in winter to protect his tender ears, and a knitted vest under his shirt in summer in case he overheated himself and caught a chill from his own sweat ...

His face was as pale and flat as a saucer of milk, and his eyes floated in it like drops of cod-liver oil. This was not so surprising as he was full to the back teeth with cod-liver oil; also with extract of malt, concentrated orange juice and calves-foot jelly. When you picked him up you expected him to squelch, like a hot-water bottle full of half-set custard.

from *Nothing to be Afraid of* by Jan Mark

Angela

If you saw Angela you would understand why I think she must be the prettiest girl in the whole world. To start with she has this lovely long golden hair that tumbles down over her shoulders and is cut in a thick fringe at the front. She's got big blue eyes like cornflowers and great long eyelashes, and rosy cheeks that dimple when she smiles which is nearly all the time. She looks as though she couldn't be naughty if she tried. Not like me.

from My Best Fiend by Sheila Lavelle

Les

Terry stared up into the strange and frightening face before him. Two slitted eyes held him there, a pair of flaking raised eyebrows and open "what're-you-going-to-do-about-it" mouth, chin up in a mocking query, dared him to move. That close, and afraid to step back into the others behind him.

Terry registered two other features in his frightened mind. The older boy's skin was paper-thin, drawn across his forehead like a very old

man's and the only hair
he seemed to have
grew in a thin dead
lock high up on
his head.

from *Terry on the Fence*
by Bernard Ashley

The finger-nail biter

... I'll just give you a detailed description of what I look like and then I can get on with the story.

Hair first: straightish with a kink at the end. It's mousy-coloured and sometimes it has a distinctly olive-green tint – honestly, I'm not exaggerating. I grew it so that I could have plaits, but it was only long enough this year and now I'm too old for plaits, so I wear it loose or in a pony-tail.

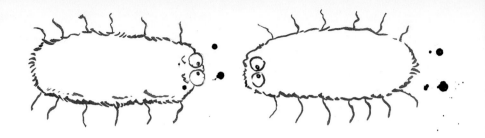

Eyebrows: two fat, furry caterpillars marching in a straight line across my forehead.

Nose: indescribable.

Mouth: cavernous. When I smile it practically goes round the back of my head.

Eyes: not bad at all considering everything else. They're greyish-green (like the hair!)

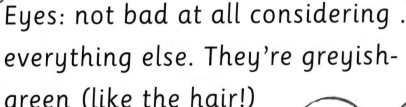

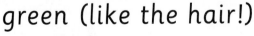

It looks as if I'm going to be at least seven feet tall by the time I've finished growing, though by some miracle I have very small hands and feet. Still, there's plenty of time for them to sprout to size eighty-nine shoes and great mangling hands.

Oh, by the way, I bite my fingernails, so the tiny hands don't look very appealing at the moment ...

from *Worlds apart* by Jill Murphy

30cms

Eric Banks

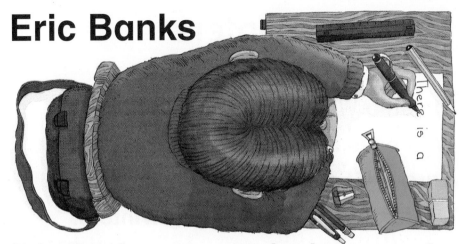

Eric Banks was a quiet boy, most of the time: "steady worker", "methodical", his school reports said. He was the kind of boy who didn't make a rush for the back seat of the bus, or go mad when the first snow fell. He was left-handed, right-footed and rather small for his age. He had freckles.

from *Woof* by Allan Ahlberg

Timothy Winters

Timothy Winters comes to school
With eyes as wide as a football pool,
Ears like bombs and teeth like splinters:
A blitz of a boy is Timothy Winters.

His belly is white, his neck is dark,
And his hair is an exclamation mark.
His clothes are enough to scare a crow
And through his britches the blue
winds blow.

from *Timothy Winters* by Charles Causley

Pearlie Mountblossom

Pearlie Mountblossom's lost her mother
she lives in a tent with her Dad and her
 brother,
she has apples for breakfast and
 Mars Bars for tea
and at night she sails the whispering sea.

from *Pearlie Mountblossom* by Helen Dunmore